FOLENS
IDEAS BANK
LOCAL HISTORY
STUDY SKILLS

Peter Hepplewhite

Neil Tonge

Contents

Folens
Publishers

How to use this book

Ideas Bank books provide ready to use, practical, photocopiable activity pages for children, **plus** a wealth of ideas for extension and development.

TEACHER IDEAS PAGE   PHOTOCOPIABLE ACTIVITY PAGE

Clear focus to the activity.

Historical background information.

Suggestions for developing work on the photocopiable pages.

Key questions.

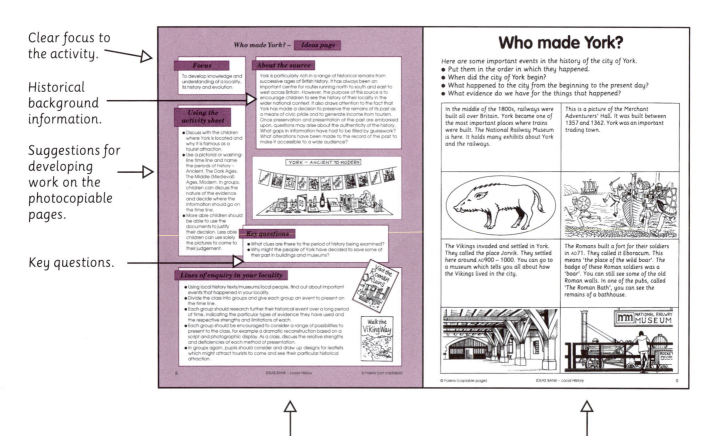

Suggested activities to follow lines of enquiry in your own locality.

Independent activities for children to work with.

The publishers wish to thank the following organisations for permission to reproduce information: Gwynedd Archives (pages 23–25), Kelly's Directories (page 19).

Folens allows photocopying of pages marked 'copiable page' for educational use, providing that this use is within the confines of the purchasing institution. Copiable pages should not be declared in any return in respect of any photocopying licence.

Peter Hepplewhite and Neil Tonge hereby assert their moral rights to be identified as the authors of this work in accordance with the Copyright, Designs and Patents Act 1988.

Editor: Alison MacTier   Layout artist: James Brown   Illustrations: Jane Bottomley, Gary Clifford, Tony O'Donnell – Graham-Cameron Illustration

Cover image: Tropical Press   Cover design: In Touch Creative Services

© 1998 Folens Limited, on behalf of the authors.

Every effort has been made to contact copyright holders of material used in this book. If any have been overlooked, we will be pleased to make any necessary arrangements.

British Library Cataloguing in Publication Data. A catalogue record for this book is available from the British Library.

First published 1998 by Folens Limited, Dunstable and Dublin.

Folens Limited, Albert House, Apex Business Centre, Boscombe Road, Dunstable, LU5 4RL, England.

ISBN 1 86202 493-6

Printed in Singapore.

Introduction

Local History Study Skills

Local history is the most flexible, and potentially the most fun, of all history studies. Whilst there is enormous scope, it also presents problems as well as opportunities. Schools can rarely buy a kit or textbook that will meet their needs – teachers must define and resource their own topic. *Ideas Bank: Local History Study Skills* offers lots of practical help. The examples given introduce a range of the main primary sources and fieldwork skills. However, this is not just a guidebook for teachers. The activity sheets and supporting ideas pages have been carefully selected to act as prompts for comparisons with your own locality and to illustrate important aspects of nineteenth- and twentieth-century Britain.

Choosing an interesting topic and developing an active approach are the key steps in local history. There are obvious links to the study of the locality in Geography and many schools prefer an integrated approach to a local area study. However, it is very easy to become guilty of antiquarianism – collecting parcels of stimulating material as an end in itself. Choosing a central question can be a useful way of focusing the topic into an investigation and avoiding a scrapbook approach. Such questions might include:

● How and why has this place changed since Victorian times?
● How difficult was life in our local Victorian workhouse?
● Why was our housing estate built by the council in 1930?
● What was life like in our town during World War II?
● What was on the site before the new river front development was built?

A good starting point is to think of the potential for fieldwork. Review what is around your school or within easy and cheap travelling distance. Think about the ordinary places as well as formal heritage sites. A church, an old hall, local shops, road and rail networks, high-rise flats, statues of famous people, leisure facilities, a nearby hospital, a nursing home or an industrial estate can all offer promising openings. If a site is on your doorstep then repeat visits can be made to clarify issues that have arisen or to check initial observations. What do the children think about the demolition of a crumbling and abandoned Victorian chapel, for example? Does it make any difference that it was the centre of community life for 100 years? Will their opinions change after they have studied the parish registers?

Few teachers live in the catchment area of their school. Yet the more they know about the community or topic the more they will capture children's enthusiasm. Lively parents, grandparents or local residents can be invaluable sources of oral history. Take the time to tape or video them formally. The local reference library, archives service and museum should be able to supply local equivalents of the documentary material shown here – maps, censuses, directories, diaries and so on. Other useful contacts might include local history societies, town guides, tourist information offices, local authority departments such as planning and engineering, and private developers. Since local history demands a good deal of research time, sympathetic headteachers may allow the use of a training day to make visits and gather resources. It's worth asking!

What is local history? – Ideas page

GREAT FIRE 1869

Focus

The purpose of the activity is to convey the idea that evidence can be drawn from a variety of sources to study a past event. Some pieces of information are more relevant than others.

Using the activity sheet

- Examine the jigsaw of possible sources and ask the children which ones they would use if they were investigating the Great Fire.
- Ask the children to list the sources in the order that they think would be of most value to them.
- Ask the children what the advantages and disadvantages of using sources are (for example, oral history may be inaccurate because people misremember).

Using sources	
Advantages	Disadvantages

Key questions

- What type of source is it?
- Why was it made?
- What are its uses?
- What are its limitations?
- If we were investigating a major historical event like the Great Fire of 1869, which of the sources would be available and which not?

About the sources

Every locality is rich in a wide range of source material:

Maps are invaluable as an immediate and visual access to the past and can indicate change in the use of the environment.

Commemorative statues and plaques can be helpful in describing particular events and indicating the significance of events to the local community.

The first nationwide census was not begun until 1801 and was subsequently taken every ten years, with the exception of 1941. Censuses tend to be more reliable and detailed after 1841.

Newspapers came into their own in the nineteenth century. Earlier examples tend to contain dense text and have no illustrations.

Oral history provides considerable opportunities for pupils to develop their listening and speaking skills.

Photographs stimulate the mind and imagination. The landscape and the dress of people can provide invaluable glimpses of the past. Videotape and film are more recent additions to the range of sources at the disposal of the historian.

Artefacts and paintings have the value of being tactile evidence which pupils can analyse and evaluate at first hand. Paintings and engravings are valuable, not only for the detail they show, but for the insight they provide into the thoughts, attitudes and feelings of people at the time.

Lines of enquiry in your locality

- Choose an event, past topic or theme. Repeat the process and ask the children to supply the types of source that would be useful in providing information.
- Ask the children to draw the person/building/event together with the range of sources that have been used for evidence.

Investigating The First World War		
Sources I have used	Pictorial evidence	
Photographs		
Churches		

What is local history?

Statues

GREAT FIRE
1869

Plaques

TOWN 1850

PARK 1870

Maps

Old buildings

Census forms 1871

NAME and Surname of each Person	RELATION to Head of Family	
James Bradley	Head	
Jane Bradley	Wife	
Georgina Bradley	Daughter	
son	Son	

Investigating The Great Fire

Sources I have used			
My questions			

The HERALD
June 1869

Newspapers

Letters

Artefacts (objects from the past)

Paintings

THE GREAT FIRE

Adverts

SMARTIES

ALWAYS DR

WOTALOTIGOT!

Oral history (what people tell us)

Videotapes

WEDDING 1981

Photographs

Who are we? – Ideas page

Focus

The example of Nottingham is used to show the range of icons that can define a locality.

Using the activity sheet

- Discuss with the children which of the icons they know and record their information on a chart.
- Using a large map of Britain, ask the children to find Nottingham. How far away is it from where they live? Using a relief map, can they discover anything about the surrounding land? Is there a forest called Sherwood? Is it still a huge forest?
- Examine each of the icons in detail. Discuss with the children what it tells us about this particular area. Are there any clues, for example the name of the football team, the trees on the badge, DH Lawrence's father was a miner and so on? (Sapienter Proficiens means progress with wisdom.)

About the source

Any locality in Britain can be chosen for this activity but in this instance Nottingham has been used because of the fame of Robin Hood and its football team. It is very unlikely that children will not have heard of Robin Hood and the Sheriff of Nottingham.

Historical research, however, strongly favours the area around Wakefield in West Yorkshire as the home of the legendary figure, Robin Hood, rather than Nottingham.

Various icons are shown on the activity page which give a range of different ways people find of defining their locality – from romantic historical personalities to foods and dialects.

Lines of enquiry in your locality

- A class survey of important things in your area provides a good starting point and a means of comparison at the end of the topic. The local tourist information office can supply a wealth of material on your locality.

Class survey of important things in Chester	
Name	Item

- Explain that the purpose behind the study is to present information about the area to a visitor. This will make obvious links with the study of a locality for Geography.
- In groups, ask the children to make a presentation of the different types of information, recipes, dialect words, famous buildings and so on. They are instructed that they can't present everything, so they must prioritise. What will they include/exclude and why?
- After making their selection, each group prepares a poster showing the things they have selected. Invite a visitor into the classroom to listen to the presentations. The children have to convince the person that their locality is the best place to come on a visit.

Key questions

- What symbols and events are chosen to represent the area in which we live?
- What does this tell us about what we think is important?

Who are we?

What is a local area? Britain is made up of lots of different areas. Each place has something special which makes it feel different from elsewhere. Here are some things for which Nottinghamshire is famous.

- Why have they chosen 'Robin Hood' as a hero?
- What do the words on the coat of arms mean?
- What do the figures and objects on the football and town badge mean?
- Design a leaflet which tells a visitor what Nottinghamshire is famous for.

A

Local heroes
Robin Hood

B

Famous people
DH Lawrence

C

SAPIENTER PROFICIENS

Coat of arms

D

FOREST

Football club
Nottingham Forest

E

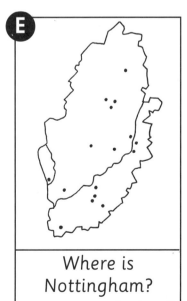

Where is
Nottingham?

F

EE'S TH' RIGHT, DUCKS?
(Are you all right, my dear?)

Local words

G

Special foods

Who made York? – *Ideas page*

Focus

To develop knowledge and understanding of a locality, its history and evolution.

About the source

York is particularly rich in a range of historical remains from successive ages of British history. It has always been an important centre for routes running north to south and east to west across Britain. However, the purpose of this source is to encourage children to see the history of their locality in the wider national context. It also draws attention to the fact that York has made a decision to preserve the remains of its past as a means of civic pride and to generate income from tourism. Once preservation and presentation of the past are embarked upon, questions may arise about the authenticity of the history. What gaps in information have had to be filled by guesswork? What alterations have been made to the record of the past to make it accessible to a wide audience?

Using the activity sheet

- Discuss with the children where York is located and why it is famous as a tourist attraction.
- Use a pictorial or washing-line time line and name the periods of history – Ancient, The Dark Ages, The Middle (Medieval) Ages, Modern. In groups, children can discuss the nature of the evidence and decide where the information should go on the time line.
- More able children should be able to use the documents to justify their decision. Less able children can use solely the pictures to come to their judgement.

YORK – ANCIENT TO MODERN

Key questions

- What clues are there to the period of history being examined?
- Why might the people of York have decided to save some of their past in buildings and museums?

Lines of enquiry in your locality

- Using local history texts/museums/local people, find out about important events that happened in your locality.
- Divide the class into groups and give each group an event to present on the time line.
- Each group should research further their historical event over a long period of time, indicating the particular types of evidence they have used and the respective strengths and limitations of each.
- Each group should be encouraged to consider a range of possibilities to present to the class, for example a dramatic reconstruction based on a script and photographic display. As a class, discuss the relative strengths and deficiencies of each method of presentation.
- In groups again, pupils should consider and draw up designs for leaflets which might attract tourists to come and see their particular historical attraction.

Visit the Roman Ruins

Walk the Viking Way

Who made York?

Here are some important events in the history of the city of York.
- Put them in the order in which they happened.
- When did the city of York begin?
- What happened to the city from the beginning to the present day?
- What evidence do we have for the things that happened?

In the middle of the 1800s, railways were built all over Britain. York became one of the most important places where trains were built. The National Railway Museum is here. It holds many exhibits about York and the railways.	This is a picture of the Merchant Adventurers' Hall. It was built between 1357 and 1362. York was an important trading town.

The Vikings invaded and settled in York. They called the place Jorvik. They settled here around AD900 – 1000. You can go to a museum which tells you all about how the Vikings lived in the city.	The Romans built a fort for their soldiers in AD71. They called it Eboracum. This means 'the place of the wild boar'. The badge of these Roman soldiers was a 'boar'. You can still see some of the old Roman walls. In one of the pubs, called 'The Roman Bath', you can see the remains of a bathhouse.

IDEAS BANK – *Local History*

Talking pictures – Ideas page

Focus

Knowledge and understanding of how paintings can represent the lifestyle of people and changes in history.

About the source

These two pictures show changes which occurred in Leeds over a vital period of British history, namely, the Industrial Revolution. They demonstrate, almost at a glance, the growth of towns, the emergence of factories and new forms of transport, for example improved roads and railways.

Art galleries in provincial towns are full of paintings depicting the surrounding landscape and representing the growth of local identity as celebrated in painting. These two pictures were produced specifically for the homes of wealthy patrons and are therefore liable to favourable interpretation.

Using the activity sheet

- Discuss with the children the effect of change on people, buildings and the environment. Children can ring the parts of the pictures which are relevant to answering the questions before they try to produce a written record.
- Explain to the children that these pictures were made to hang on the walls of the homes of wealthy people in Leeds. If they were factory owners what would they want to see in their picture? If they were local rich people what would they want to see in their picture? What might be missed out from such scenes to please these people?

A picture of Leeds

Evidence	Information
factory owner	
wealthy people	
historical information	
photographs	

- What other evidence do we need, apart from the pictures, to get a more accurate understanding of life in Leeds at these two times? Make a table to record your findings.
- Collectors of paintings often enjoyed scenes which told a story with a powerful moral message. To demonstrate the changes that might occur, set up a scene of children queuing up in front of a workhouse. How will they be arranged to make the viewer look more sympathetically upon their plight? Freeze-frame the children in a similar way for a photographic activity.

Key questions

- What does the painting show?
- When was it painted?
- How might the artist have selected particular features and why?

Lines of enquiry in your locality

- A visit to a local art gallery focused on paintings of local views can give children an instant view of the past. Children can make an outline sketch of what they see. They should label buildings they can identify and provide dates for the paintings.
- As an alternative, many galleries will have postcards of their local collections. These can be accompanied by similar questions to those on the activity sheet.

Talking pictures

Leeds in Yorkshire was an important centre for the sale of woollen cloth from the early 1700s. With the invention of the steam engine and machines for making cloth, smoky factories grew up. Pictures like these two of Leeds can tell us a great deal about the changes that happened in the local area.

A view of Leeds in 1715

A view of Leeds in 1846

● How many years have passed between the time the two pictures were made?
● What has happened to the size of Leeds?
● What new buildings can you see in the picture of 1846 that weren't there in 1715?
● What types of transport can you see in the picture of 1715?
● What type of transport can you see in the picture of 1846?
● What changes might there be to people's lives in Leeds – if they were poor? If they were rich?
● Why might these pictures have been painted?
● What else do you need to know before you can say whether life was better or worse for people who lived in Leeds in 1846 than it had been in 1715?

Change over time – Ideas page

Focus

- To show the development of land use using Ordnance Survey maps.

Using the activity sheet

- Looking at each map, pick out and discuss changes such as roads, housing types, local facilities, transport. Compare these with your area, for example typical 1930s semis, Map 2.
- Use a ruler to estimate distances, 1cm=30 metres. For example, how long was Henderson Terrace in 1895 and in 1940? Describe the changes.
- Colour-code the maps and lightly shade in features, for example green for open spaces, brown for buildings, grey for roads. What has happened to the open spaces on Map 1?
- Draw 1cm or 2cm grids on to clear overlays to estimate land use. Count up squares showing fields or housing and display the results in block graphs.
- Describe what you would pass if walking this route in 1895, 1940 and 1997.

Route walked	1895	1940	1997

Start at the corner of Westwood Street and Henderson Terrace. Walk along Henderson Terrace. Turn right down Kayll Road. Turn right at Chester Road. Walk along Chester Road. Stop at the end of Chester Road.

About the source

Ordnance Survey maps make a wonderful starting point for local history. Since the late eighteenth century, the OS has mapped the British Isles at a variety of scales including 1:2500 and 1:10560 (25" and 6" to the mile) county maps. In 1945 a National Grid was set up and a system of continuous revision adopted. The 1:2500 maps offer remarkable detail. The 1:10560 maps are useful for an overview, for example showing a town or village in the context of the surrounding countryside. Current maps can generally be ordered from local authority planning departments. A standard working scale for planners today is 1:1250 (10" to the mile). The sequential 1:2500 maps on the activity sheets show developments in a small area of urban Sunderland over 100 years. The scale has been reduced to fit the page and is 1:3000.

Key questions

- What kind of transport is only shown on Map 2?
- Why does it not appear on Maps 1 and 3?
- What are allotments (Map 2)? What happened to them (Map 3)?
- What different kinds of housing can be seen?

Lines of enquiry in your locality

- Obtain large-scale OS maps for an investigation of your locality. Compile a list of questions and sites to visit.

An investigation of our town
When was the nearby street built?
Who lived there?
How has the street changed?

- Use fieldwork and research to answer the questions. Sketch, photograph and describe surviving features. Collect primary sources, such as censuses and photographs, to show past developments. Make a display of questions and materials which give the answers.
- Compare developments in your area with those on the activity sheets. How are they the same or different?

Change over time
OS Map 1

- The Ordnance Survey, often shortened to OS, has made detailed maps of Britain since 1800. This map shows an area of a Victorian town in 1895. List and describe the features you can see.

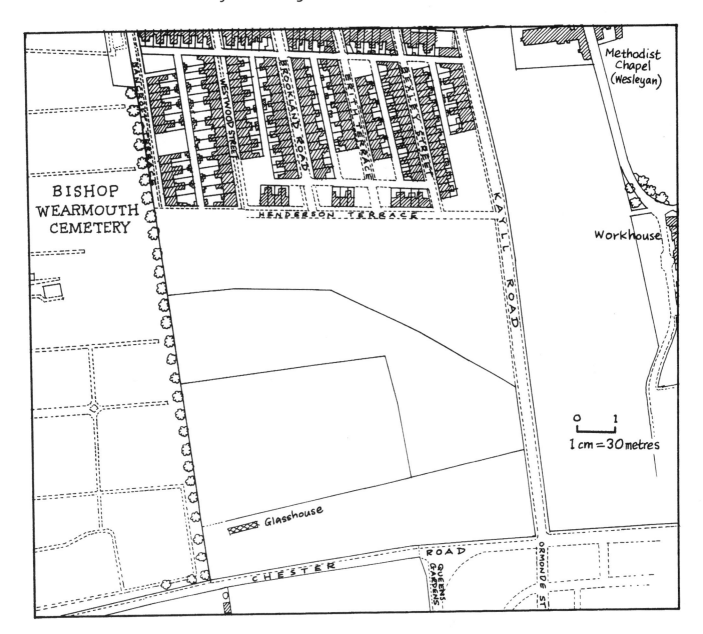

 • Compare Map 1 with Map 2.

Change over time
OS Map 2

● This map was made in 1940. Look carefully and fill in the table.

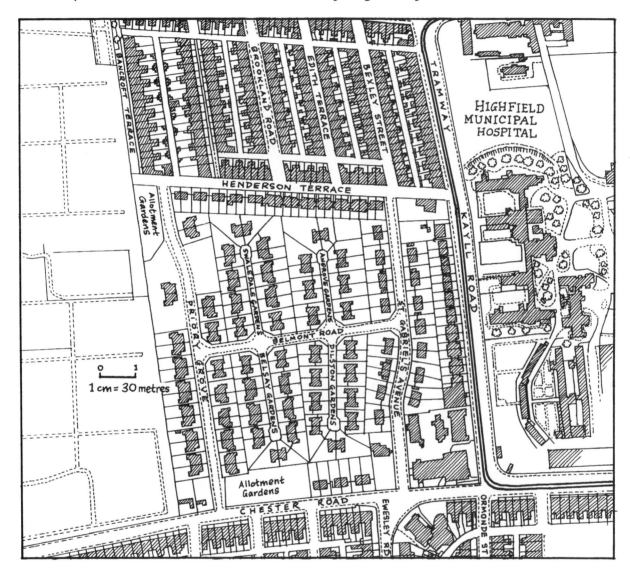

● What has changed and what has stayed the same since 1895?

These features have stayed the same	These features have changed

● Compare Map 2 with Map 3.

IDEAS BANK – *Local History* © Folens (copiable page)

Change over time
OS Map 3

● This map was made in 1997. Look carefully and fill in the table.

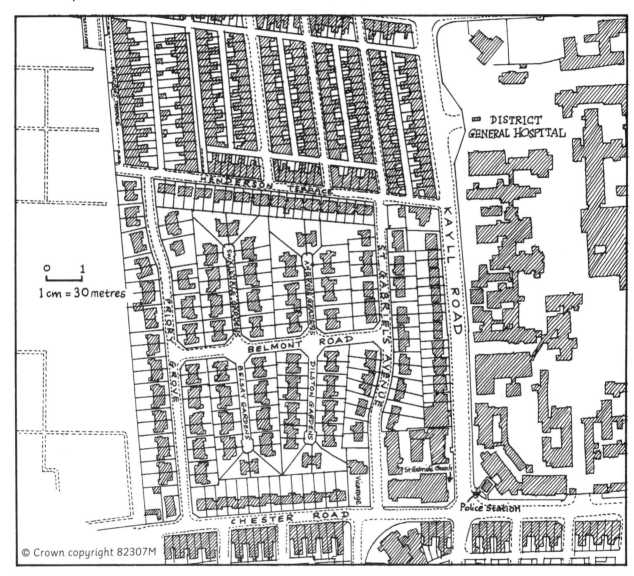

© Crown copyright 82307M

1 cm = 30 metres

● What has changed and what has stayed the same since 1940?

These features have stayed the same	These features have changed

● Look at Maps 1–3. What do you think has been the most important change between 1895 and 1997? Explain your answer.

Healthy homes –

Focus

To show the development of house construction and town planning by examining local plans.

Using the activity sheet

- On the plan, convert the imperial measurements to metric (1 foot = 0.3048 metre) and draw the full-size plan in chalk in the playground. Use string and canes to get straight lines. Draw outlines of furniture. How are the flats in these houses heated? How many fireplaces are there? Point out the copper or boiler in the scullery. Discuss the advantages and disadvantages of coal fires/modern central heating.
- Look at the WCs and drains. Discuss the importance of these facilities at a time when houses commonly made use of excreta tubs, emptied weekly by midden or night soil men.
- How are doors, windows, steps, stairs, fireplaces and drains shown? Make a key.

About the source

The cholera epidemics of the 1830s–40s pushed Parliament into passing laws to improve town planning. Local councils were given powers to specify standards and developers had to submit plans for approval. Many of these local authority collections survive in the care of their archive services, especially for the late Victorian period onwards. They are among the best sources historians have for the physical growth of towns. Details usually include plans and elevations, dates, sections through the site, measurements and details of construction. The latter are particularly helpful in the classroom.

front elevation

Lines of enquiry in your locality

- Identify housing types and buildings near your school and order copies of the building plans.
- Compare the plans with the existing building. Make a note of any changes. Discuss the kinds of modernisation that may occur over the years, for example re-roofing, new windows, electricity instead of gas, changes in materials.

Changes to the Town Hall	
Modernisation	Reason for change
roof	
windows	

Key questions

- Why does the house have two front doors?
- Are the flats for large or small families? How many people could live comfortably in each flat?
- What is the difference between the scullery and the kitchen? (Scullery used for washing.)
- Where are the toilets? Why are they outside?
- What are the small figures on the walls? (Thickness of walls.)

KEY

	fireplace		door
	oven		boiler
	window		fireplace

- Write out directions to move from one part of a building to another. For example, on the activity sheet, walk from the front door of the lower flat to the WC.

Healthy homes

● In Victorian times local councils first began to check the standard of new buildings. Plans had to be approved before a house could be built. Look at this plan of a pair of flats in Newcastle-upon-Tyne and fill in this table.

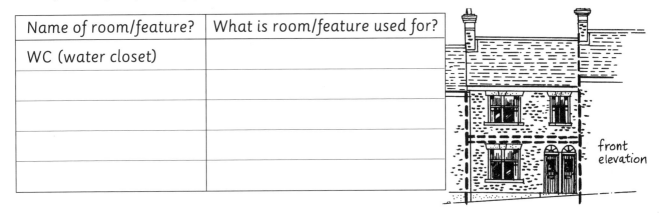

front elevation

Name of room/feature?	What is room/feature used for?
WC (water closet)	

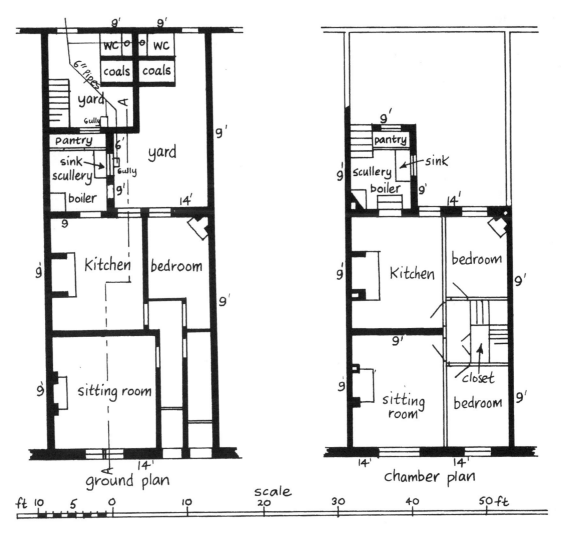

ground plan

chamber plan

scale
ft 10   5   0   10   20   30   40   50 ft

● How are the flats different?
What are the advantages and disadvantages of each?

Street directories – Ideas page

Focus

Using street directories as a resource for local business and community information.

About the source

Street directories were published in county or town volumes for most of the nineteenth century and lingered on until the 1960s. They were made redundant by the growth in telephone use and directories such as the Yellow Pages or the Thomson Local directory. A good street directory has several features which are invaluable for local history.

Individual entries may be listed by street, in alphabetical order or by trade. Often each community has a brief history and a summary of economic activity, public institutions and welfare provision (such as schools, churches and chapels). Adverts feature prominent local businesses and can be illustrated.

Street directories can give us a wide social sweep, from lords to common lodging house keepers. However, since it was necessary to subscribe or pay a fee to be included, they do not list every property. A much fuller picture is given of commercial and wealthier areas.

Using the activity sheet

- Use dictionaries to make a glossary of some of the more difficult terms, for example:
  alabaster – a cheap, easily carved version of marble,
  portmanteau – a travelling bag,
  ironmonger – selling the metal parts for horses' fittings.
- Design and draw shop signs for the businesses in Lisle Street. Display these in numerical order.
- Make a table dividing the businesses into manufacturers, retailers and services. Do any businesses fit in more than one category?

	Manufacturer	Retailer	Service
Falcon			
Dorey Henry			
Stevens George			

- Street directories illustrate the economic growth of communities. Discuss who would be likely to use them. How would they help businesses find customers and customers find goods and services?
- Look at pictures of Victorian military uniforms. What would a military embroiderer make? (Flags, colours, cap badges, arm badges and so on.)

Lines of enquiry in your locality

- Make a school directory, giving location, name, and speciality.

School Directory		
Location	Name	Speciality

- Obtain directory entries for an older shopping street near the school. If it is a Victorian street, look for continuity and change over time, for example pinpoint the 1890s, 1930s and 1960s.
- Compare the 1890s entry with the 1891 census and find out how many owners lived above their businesses. What were their families like?
- Use fieldwork to make an up-to-date shopping survey and street directory. If you are using a well-established shopping area, detailed *Goadplans* may be available. Prepare tables similar to those above, showing change in types of high-street businesses.

Key questions

- Where could you buy the coach?
- Where would you buy newspapers and stationery?
- Where could you stay for a night in Lisle Street?
- How many women have businesses?

Street directories

Before telephone directories like the Yellow Pages, street directories helped people find the goods and services they needed. This example is taken from The Post Office Directory for London, 1874.

- The equipment for this horse was bought in Lisle Street. Look carefully at the picture and copy and complete the table.
- What do the letters 'Geo', 'Edwd' and 'Co' mean? Make a table of these shortened words and show what they would be in full.
- Why do you think there was no number 13 in Lisle Street?

Lisle street, 9 & 10 *Princes street, Leicester square.* (**W.**)

1 *Falcon,* John Evans
2 Dorey Henry, newsagent
3 Stevens Geo. alabastr.ornamt.ma
  Arnold Richard, engraver
4 Elliot Wm. R. leather warehouse
5 Abraham R. & Sons, military embroiderers
  Peake Mrs. Sophia, coach manfr
6 Millard Edwd.who.portmntu.ma
7 Owen John Allington, saddler
8 Horton Charles, harness plater

9 Hall George, plumber &c
10 Hall Wm. Thomas, carpenter
11 Wright Thos.watch&clock maker
12 *Royal Society of Musicians,*
        Stanley Lucas, sec
14 Pinches Thos. Ryan &Co.manfrs.
    of envelopes & gen. stationers
15 King Robert Kingcote & Henry & Co. bridle cutters
16 Kerteux Madame Annette,lodg.ho
17 Aked Mrs. Elizth. wardrobe dealr
18 Lockwood Fredk. R. carpenter
19 Clark Howard, surgeon
19&20 Green I.&Co.saddlers' irnmgrs

Equipment	Maker and job
bit	

Letters	Complete word
Geo	

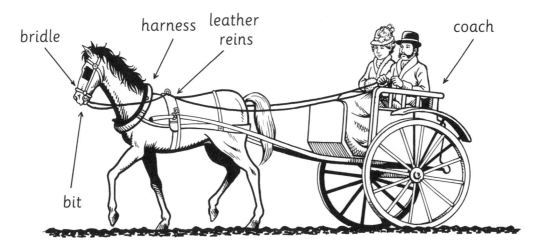

bridle · harness · leather reins · coach · bit

- Find out why so many businesses were making equipment for horses in 1874.

Looking at a Victorian family – Ideas page

Focus

Using census information to identify the lifestyle and structure of family groups in history.

Using the activity sheet

● Explain to the children the meanings of the abbreviated words in the census.

● Discuss what a census is and the reasons why census information can help governments meet the needs of people today, for example, the number of school places required, family size and structure and likely future housing needs.

● Divide the children into pairs – enumerator and Mr Bradley. Assume Mr Bradley can't write. The enumerator must ask questions and fill in a blank form for him. How might mistakes be made and incorrect information be recorded?

● Discuss the last question on the pupil page. Divorce was out of the question for a working-class Victorian family. It is likely that Mr Gibson had died and Mrs Gibson had remarried. Why might she want to do this?

About the source

The census has been taken every ten years since 1801, with the exception of 1941. Thousands of enumerators were appointed to issue, collect and check household forms. The information on the forms was then copied into master volumes.

Enumerators' books are stored at the Public Record Office, but microfilms covering 1841–1891 are currently available in most local reference libraries. They list, by household and institution, every person present on the night of the census, giving name, marital status, age, sex, relationship to the head of the household, occupation and place of birth. The raw data is not released to the public for 100 years. However, statistical breakdowns are published and used by local authorities and the government.

Key questions

● How many people were in the Bradley/Gibson household?
● How many males?
● How many females?
● Who is the oldest person?
● Who is the youngest?

Lines of enquiry in your locality

● Give the children a blank census form and ask them to complete it for their own family (or a made-up family if home circumstances are delicate).

● Obtain census information for a house or street near your school. Link to fieldwork, choosing a road that will be safe and easily supervised. In new towns or estates, look out for past farmsteads. Most schools will be able to find an example within walking distance of their location.

● Read and transcribe the enumerators' handwriting for one or two households.

● Census material offers one of the best opportunities for the use of IT in History. Enter the details of 50/100 people on a database such as Junior Pinpoint by Longman Logotron. Spreadsheet printouts can help those children unable to cope with the original text. Display data graphically, such as age patterns or sex ratios. Many local authorities use the last census to prepare ward profiles. These are invaluable for the study of the locality in Geography. Compare them with information on the Victorian sheets, for example types of jobs held by men and women.

Looking at a Victorian family

This family lived in the centre of Newcastle. Their details were written down in the census of 1881.

- Who is the head of the family? _____

  Where does he come from? _____

  Who is his wife? _____

  Where does she come from? _____

- Is this a poor family? Explain your answer.

  _____

  _____

  _____

- How many of the children are working? What are their jobs?

  _____

  _____

- Some of the people in this family are called Bradley and others are called Gibson. Can you explain why this might be so? Use the back of the sheet to give your answer.

Name and surname	Relation	Age last Birthday	Rank, profession, or OCCUPATION	Where born
James Bradley	Head	40	Boot and shoe maker	Ireland
Jane Bradley	Wife	42		Newcastle Upon Tyne
Georgina Gibson	Daug	18	Dress maker	do
George Gibson	Son	16	Barber	do
William Gibson	Son	14	mess. Errand Boy	do
John Gibson	Son	13	Scholar	do
Sarah Gibson	Daug	10	Scholar	do
Jane Bradley	Daug	5	Scholar	do

Parish people – Ideas page

Focus

Parish registers can usefully link local history to national history.

Using the activity sheet

- Discuss the type of information shown and how this helps us build a picture of a community, for example age at marriage and death, occupations, addresses, numbers entered per year.
- Look up the town of Carnarvon (Caernarfon) in an atlas. What county is it in now? (Gwynedd.)
- Look at the number of infants in the burial register. What can you find out about the causes? (From the 1870s local Medical Officer of Health reports give infant mortality rates. They were commonly as high as 20–25% of live births.)
- Look at the diary on page 25 to stimulate class discussion. The first line could suggest a happy ending spoiled – a master and servant fall in love but mother and love child die. However, it is more likely that David abandoned Elizabeth and was relieved of an embarrassment by her death. Had he wished it the child could have been given his name on the baptism register. Surviving unmarried mothers often ended up in the workhouse.

About the source

In 1538 English and Welsh parish churches were first instructed to keep a register of baptisms, marriages and burials. Since 1813, specially printed registers have been used, with separate books for each type of service. The examples on the activity sheets show those used by the Church of England and Nonconformist churches. Catholic registers use a different form and are usually in Latin. The earliest surviving registers for the Church of Scotland (Presbyterian) start in 1560. For the period before the census, historians rely heavily on parish registers to build profiles of communities and compile population estimates.

Key questions

- What is unusual about the Roberts family? (John has married twice and is bringing the children from both marriages to be baptised.)
- What does parish mean? (The area served by a church.) What and where are your local Church of England, Wales, Ireland or Scotland, and Catholic churches?
- On sheet 1, what was different about the birth of David Williams?
- What problems might David's mother have faced?
- On the burial register (p.25), who died in prison (gaol)?

Lines of enquiry in your locality

- Make a class family history display using birth, marriage and death certificates, or if this raises too many personal problems, show copies belonging to older people. How are they similar and different to parish registers?

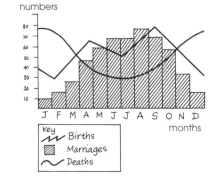

- Obtain a five-year run of register entries and use these for statistical work. Display information graphically and try to identify patterns such as sex and age ratios, the most popular months for marriages and the worst months for deaths.

Name	Abode	Month of marriage	Month of death

- Use the abode column to plot addresses on a local map. How big was the parish? Where did most people live?
- Link register entries to census entries and build profiles of local families.
- Cross reference burial registers with a visit to the church cemetery. What additional information do grave inscriptions give?

Parish people – births

- For nearly 500 years churches have kept parish registers of the baptisms, marriages and burials of local people. Look carefully at this page from a register of baptisms at St Beblig's Church in Wales.

In which town was St Beblig's? ______________________

How many children were baptised? ________ boys ________ girls

Who do you think the first two children are named after?

____

Born Sept^{m} 20th 1856

When baptised	Child's Christian name	Parent's name: Christian	Parent's name: Surname	Abode	Quality, trade or profession	By whom the ceremony was performed
1865 Dec 14th	John Richard	John Richard and Tabitha Grace	Roberts	Glandwfr Carnarvon	Merchant	James Vincent, Vicar.
1865 Dec 14th	Tabitha Grace	John Richard and Tabitha Grace	Roberts	Glandwfr Carnarvon	Merchant	James C Vincent, Carnarvon. Vicar
1865 Dec 14th	Fanny Jane	John Richard and Lumley Jane	Roberts	Glandwfr Carnarvon	Merchant	James C Vincent carnarvon, Vicar
1865 Dec 14th	William Griffith	John Richard and Lumley Jane	Roberts	Glandwfr Carnarvon	Merchant	James C. Vincent, Carnarvon, Vicar.
1865 Dec 21st	David (illegitimate son of)	Elizabeth and David	Williams. Jones	–	Servant Maid Gentleman	Norman Jenkins, curate

Parish people – marriages

This certificate comes from the marriage register at St Beblig's.

- Who is being married?

  Husband _____ Aged _____

  Wife _____ Aged _____

- What can we tell about William Roberts' past life? How do we know Harriet Jones couldn't write?
- Do you think they are a rich couple? Explain your answer.

_____

_____

_____

_____

18*65* Marriage solemnized at *the Parish Church* in the *Parish* of *Llanbeblig* in the County of *Carnarvon*

No.	When married	Name and surname	Age	Condition	Rank or profession	Residence at time of marriage	Father's name or surname	Rank or profession of Father
65	Dec 7th	William Roberts	26	Widower	Mariner	Parish of Clynnog	William Roberts	Blacksmith
		Harriet Jones	21	Spinster	—	Bangor st Carnarvon	Robert Jones	Labourer

Married in the *Parish Church* according to the Rites and Ceremonies of the Established Church, by *License* or after_____ by me, *James Vincent, Vicar*

This Marriage was solemnized between us. { *William Roberts* / *Harriet Jones her ✗ Mark* } in the Presence of us, { *Thomas Roberts* / *Ellen Jones, her ✗ mark* }

- Imagine it is 1880 and you are either Peter Flynn, aged 29 or Dorothy Turnbull, aged 19. Make a bigger copy of this certificate and fill in the rest of the details for your marriage. What is the date? Who are you marrying? Where do you live?

Parish people – burials

Here is a page from the 1865 burial register at St Beblig's.

● Who is the youngest person to be buried at St Beblig's that week?

Name _____   Age _____

Who is the oldest person to be buried that week?

Name _____   Age _____

● Shade in this pie chart to show the number of males and females buried from December 20–26, 1865.

Name	Abode	When buried	Age	By whom ceremony was performed
Mary Ellen Edwards	Henwaliau Carnarvon	Dec 20th	1 month	John Lewis, Curate
Catherine Rowlands	S. Penrallt Carnarvon	Dec 21st	61 years	John Lewis, Curate
David Becs	Gaol Carnarvon	Dec 22nd	64 years	John Lewis, Curate
Elizabeth Williams	Segontium Terr. Carnarvon	Dec 23rd	25 years	John Lewis, Curate
David Williams	Segontium Terr. Carnarvon	Dec 23rd	2 weeks	John Lewis, Curate
Aurthur John Poole	Pwlheli Road Carnarvon	Dec 25th	1 week	James Vincent Vicar
William Perry	N. Penrallt Carnarvon	Dec 26th	62 years	John Lewis, Curate

● Find Elizabeth Williams on sheets 1 and 3. David Jones was the father of her child. Finish this entry in his diary. What is their sad story? Put in as many details as you can.

My plans to marry Elizabeth are cruelly snatched away …

Moving north – Ideas page

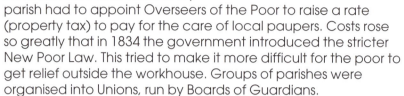

Focus

Looking at problems faced by a poor family in history and the help they could expect from the State.

About the source

The old Poor Law was set up between 1597 and 1601. Every parish had to appoint Overseers of the Poor to raise a rate (property tax) to pay for the care of local paupers. Costs rose so greatly that in 1834 the government introduced the stricter New Poor Law. This tried to make it more difficult for the poor to get relief outside the workhouse. Groups of parishes were organised into Unions, run by Boards of Guardians.

 Before 1834, the records of Parish Overseers and after 1834, the records of Poor Law Unions build a vivid profile of the lives of 'paupers' and the attitudes of those who looked after them. Look out for Overseers', or Guardians' minutes, workhouse plans, admissions registers and diet sheets. The activity sheet is adapted from the First Annual Report of the Poor Law Commissioners, 1835. Similar volumes, packed with short reports for most areas of the country, were published for the next hundred years.

Using the activity sheet

- Dr Kay interviewed Samuel Blick for his report. Make a list of the questions he may have asked.

Dr Kay's questions
1. What are the names of your family?
2. What are their ages?
3.

- Ask the children to describe three advantages of moving for the Blick family.
- Dr Kay's report argued that it was good for poor families to move from the southern countryside to northern towns. Discuss what the disadvantages might be for some families (for example leaving friends and family or worse living and working conditions).
- How would an oven, grate, slopstones (a large, shallow sink for washing clothes) and boiler make life easier for Mrs Blick? Draw a diagram of each of these and explain how they would be used.

Key questions

- How large was the Blick family?
- How might they have felt about moving?
- The parish paid for them to move. Why do you think they did this?

I am Edward Wilson.
I am eighty-five.
I can no longer work.

Lines of enquiry in your locality

- Use Overseers'/Vestry minutes to find out the kind of help given to the poor by the parish – bread, clothes, money, nursing/medical care, burial, employment.
- Set up a role play. Some children are paupers applying for relief (help), for example "I am Edward Wilson. I am 85. I can no longer work and my landlord has put me on the street. I have nothing but the clothes I stand in." Others are the Overseers/Guardians who have to decide what will be done for them.
- Obtain copies of the census (see page 20) for 1851 for your local workhouse. Who were the poor? Old people, children, young men?
- Many workhouses evolved into local hospitals. Find out where your local workhouse was and what happened to it. Use OS maps (see page 13) to find out about site changes.

Moving north

Before the Blick family moved:

◆ Samuel Blick, aged 39, moved with his wife, aged 41, and eight children from Princes Risborough in Buckinghamshire. He earned 8s (40p) a week as a farmer's labourer. Before that he was on the parish, working on the roads.

◆ His wife and two girls earned 2s (10p) making lace pillows.

◆ William aged 19, had been out of work for two weeks before they left. Before this he had 2s 6d ($12\frac{1}{2}$p) from the parish.

◆ John, aged 15, was a servant with a farmer. He was given food, lodgings and £2 a year, but did not earn enough to help the family. Henry, aged 13, was a ploughboy and earned 2s.

◆ Sophy, aged 12, did not work.

◆ The family's total earnings and allowances were 14s 6d ($72\frac{1}{2}$p) a week. Samuel paid 1s 6d ($7\frac{1}{2}$p) for a miserable cottage with a broken brick floor. There were three rooms.

After the Blick family moved:

Samuel now works in the small town of Stalybridge, near Manchester, at the cotton mills of W. Harrison and Brothers.

		Old and new pence
◆ Samuel, labourer, earns 12s (60p) per week		
◆ Wife, housewife		s = shilling
◆ William, labourer, earns 11s (55p)		d = old pence
◆ John, foundry (iron works) 8s (40p)		1 shilling = 12d
◆ Henry, factory 3s (15p)		20 shillings = £1
◆ Sophy, ill.		
◆ Sally, aged 11, factory 2s (10p)		
◆ Reuben, aged 9; Mary, aged 7; Alfred, aged 4 – not employed.		

The Blicks have a good stone cottage, with four rooms, an oven, grate, slopstones and boiler for 2s 6d ($12\frac{1}{2}$p) per week. Samuel has more and better food, a better house, a kinder master and is well treated by his new workmates.

From Dr Kay's Report on the Migration of Labourers, 1835.

● Copy the headings in this table and fill it in for all the Blick family.

Name	Age	Job at Princes Risborough	Job at Stalybridge
Samuel Blick			

Collecting the evidence – Ideas page

Using the activity sheet

- Discuss the working conditions of the girls. Why might employers and parents want children working in the mines? Ask the children to work out a Scots/standard English glossary of Margaret's words.

Glossary

na	=	no
sair	=	sore
gai	=	very

- Fill a rucksack with 25 kilos of rocks or books. How many children can lift this? How far can they carry it? ⚠️

- Use the illustration to ask the children what employers might think of the CEC. Many believed it was biased. Their reasons included interviews with ignorant children, inspectors giving personal opinions rather than facts, and dislike of government interference.

About the source

A major feature of government since 1800 is the collection of evidence on a rapidly changing country. A huge series of royal commissions, parliamentary select committees and annual reports of various boards and ministries gave the government a wealth of information that often led to useful reforms. Collectively these are known as the 'blue books' or parliamentary papers.

The example on the activity sheet is adapted from the *Children's Employment Commission*, hereafter CEC (1842). This was inspired by Lord Shaftesbury, with inspectors visiting dozens of industries using child labour, for example paper making in Kent and the hosiery trade in Nottingham. The volume on mines led to the 1842 Mines Act which abolished female labour underground and excluded boys under ten years.

I am a miner. I think Mr Frank's report is rubbish because...

Key questions

- Why might girls be better workers than boys?
- What jobs do the girls do? How are they different?
- How long does Ellison work? How long does she sleep?
- What do the girls think of their work?

Lines of enquiry in your locality

- Ask your local reference library to locate a copy of the CEC. Use the contents pages to identify industries using child labour in your area. Ask advice on any other good parliamentary papers covering local issues such as education or public health.
- Copy a series of interviews with children from the CEC. Use these for inspector/respondent role plays.
- Inspectors in royal commissions had powers to compel people to answer them. In the CEC who might not want to answer and why?
- The CEC and other reports informed and influenced public opinion. Write newspaper articles, outline the problems and suggest reforms.
- Discuss modern government investigations such as the Cullen Inquiry into the shooting of primary school children at Dunblane.

Collecting the evidence

In Scotland girls and women are employed alongside males in the coal mines. Generally girls start work at an earlier age than boys because their parents think they are brighter and capable of making themselves more useful. I have seen women and girls coal bearing. This labour is cruel, slaving and revolting to humanity. Yet I found a six year old, Margaret Levinson, at this work. Margaret told me: "Been down at coal carrying six weeks; carry full 56lb (25kilos) of coal in a wooden tub. The work is na guid; it is so very sair; I work with sister Jesse and mother; dinna ken the time we gang; it is gai dark." A second girl, 11 year old Ellison Jack told me:

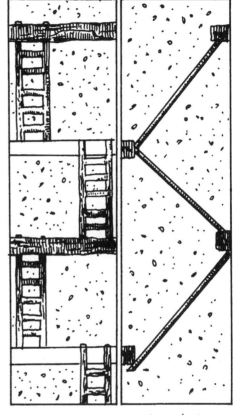

trap staircase   sectional view of trap stair

"I have been working below three years. My father takes me down at two in the morning and I come up at one or two next afternoon. I go to bed at six at night to be ready for work. I have to carry my load up four traps or ladders. My task is to fill four or five tubs, each tub holds 4 1/2 cwt (225 kilos). I fill five tubs in 20 journeys. I have had the strap when I did not do my bidding. Am very glad when my task is wrought, as it sore tires me."

Ellison's work is to carry a basket, shaped like a cockle shell, from the coal face to the tubs at the bottom of the shaft. This basket allows lumps of coal to rest on the back of the neck and shoulders. It often takes more than one man to lift the burden on to her back.

R H Franks Esquire, Sub Commissioner for East Scotland

● Think about the dangers Margaret and Ellison faced at work and copy and complete the table. What would you suggest to make their jobs safer?

Dangers faced by the girls	My safety recommendations

● Now make a list of the questions you think the inspector asked the girls. What others would you have asked?

Problems at school – Ideas page

Focus

Using log books as a resource for the development of schools.

My name is Harry Miles. I'm not having my lad waste his time.

Using the activity sheet

- Ask the head teacher if he/she will show the current school log book to the children and read out some recent entries. What kind of events are included? Why does the head have to do this? (Some schools have slipped into the unfortunate habit of putting items of significance into governors' minutes only. This denies an historical source to future generations.)
- Compulsory education did not begin until 1880. Discuss how the head of Eling School might try to convince parents that their children should attend regularly.
- Use the illustration on this page to give the anti-school views of some parents (children better off working, family needs the money, can't afford the fee – 2d a week).
- Keep a class log book, making a note of any special events or incidents. Ask a different child to write an entry each day.

About the source

From 1862 schools requiring a government grant had to keep a log book and were paid according to results. Instructions to HMIs inspecting these commented:
"A teacher who performs this duty simply with discrimination will find it a powerful help in mastering his profession as well as an honourable monument of his duties."
Log books can be particularly vivid for the Victorian period, at best giving the social context of the school. Look out for other education records such as admission registers, punishment books, LEA circulars and plans.

Key questions

- Why would the head teacher in Source A be concerned that lots of families were moving in and out of the area?
- How is the school year different in Source B?
- How might the children in Source B feel at school? Do you think they liked working?

Lines of enquiry in your locality

- Obtain a range of log book entries for older schools in your area. Check prominent dates, for example, Queen Victoria's Diamond Jubilee in 1897, or wartime evacuation in 1939. Look out for local events such as the effects of the 1926 strike in mining areas. Read the entries to the children and make an education time line.

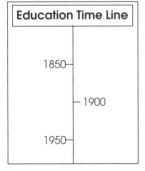

Education Time Line

1850–

1900

1950–

- HMI reports are a common feature of log books. What lessons are the same and different now? Make the information into a 'then and now' chart. How is the school doing? Try some Victorian/Edwardian lessons such as recitation, drill, needlework, spelling. Role play an HMI visit during a spelling test.

Then	Now
Drill	
Recitation	

- Log books in record offices are closed to the public for 30 years from the last entry. What is the purpose of this rule? (Confidentiality, personal details of staff and children are sometimes included.)

Problems at school

Headteachers have to keep a log book or diary of school events.
These two entries are from country schools in Hampshire.

Source A – Eling National School
December, 1877:
Many of the boys attend very poorly being away from school half their time. The excuses made for absence and coming late are frivolous, "Had to get groceries in for mother. Had to fetch a pound of soda." Many do not know why they stop away or come late. Increased attendance would mean an increased grant.

Source B Chandler's Ford Church of England School
Log Book October 31st
End of the School Year, 1894:
Fifty-two children have been admitted. The movement of families is greater than ever. The brickyard employs a great number of boys from early morning until ten o'clock and immediately after school they have to trudge off to work again till dark. They are in consequence tired out before school time and it is doubly difficult to interest an already overworked child. Scarcely a boy received a scripture lesson during the whole summer.

- What excuses are the children in Source A giving for being late? Why is the head annoyed about this? _____

_____

- What are many of the boys in Source B doing before and after school? How is this affecting them at school? _____

_____

- Imagine you are the head of Chandler's Ford School. Write a letter to the manager of the brickworks telling him your views about children working.

Smile please! – Ideas page

Focus

Using photographs as evidence of changes in school conditions.

About the source

The nineteenth century witnessed a growth in the number of elementary schools together with the government's increasing (if reluctant) involvement. Supporters of government intervention were keen to demonstrate the beneficial effects of elementary education on children both mentally and physically.

These two pictures, based on photographs, were included in evidence submitted to the Parliamentary Committee Report on Physical Deterioration in 1904. The Boer War of 1899–1902 had revealed a considerable proportion of the recruits as being unsuitable for military service and this spread fear as to Britain's world role. In this instance the supporters of elementary education wished to demonstrate its beneficial effects.

Using the activity sheet

- Most schools will have a collection of class photographs. The further they go back the better. In addition, teachers may have their own examples which they can use to show change.
- Discuss with the children the differences they can see. Provide magnifying glasses so they can observe detail.
- In groups give the children two photographs, separated in time, and allow them to list the differences they can detect.

1950	1990
Uniform	No uniform

- In groups, present the differences they have observed. Arrange the photographs in chronological order and draw out the main changes.
- Discuss why school photographs are taken, who would want them and where they might be kept or displayed.

Key questions

- What does the picture show?
- Is there a particular reason why the picture was taken?
- How might the reason affect the way the picture was taken?

Lines of enquiry in your locality

- Each pupil can adopt the pose of a child in the later photograph and 'freeze-frame'. Take the photograph, then each child should draw a bubble from their head. Inside the bubble pupils write down the answers to the following questions: how are you dressed? what are you feeling? what happens after the photograph is taken?
- Discuss how different photographs may be taken of the same children but for different purposes.
- Now pose the children in such a way that will give the impression of the earlier class. (Note how many of the children in the photograph are holding books.)
- Take a second photograph after discussing how they might show a very bad school.

Smile please!

These two pictures are based on photographs of boys from the Lant School in London. They were used to show how boys' health had got better between 1874 and 1902.

- How are the boys dressed in the first picture?
- How are they dressed in the second picture?
- Do they look better?
- Why have the boys in the first picture been given books to hold?
- This was a very poor school. Would they have had lots of books?

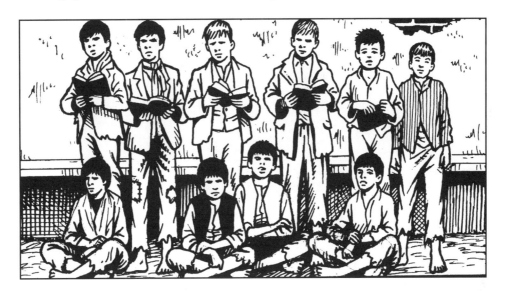

These pictures were put together to show that boys had become healthier.
- Does this mean that boys everywhere became healthier?
- How might they have made the boys in the second picture look healthier?

War memories – Ideas page

Focus

Knowledge and understanding of oral history to illustrate the development of lifestyles.

About the source

One of the most vivid recollections of older generations is the period of World War II, when social life was disrupted on a massive scale. The three extracts are reminiscences about evacuation during that war. As with all historical events, people's experiences differ according to their particular circumstances – age, sex, class, family and temperament.

Using the activity sheet

- The extracts are meant to demonstrate a range of views and are intended to act as a lead into the value of oral reminiscences as part of a local study.
- Pupils will need to know what evacuation was and why it occurred. Discuss how particular interpretations of the past have come about.
- Older members of the community can be interviewed and their experiences added to the three extracts provided. Pupils can make comparisons between the extracts and the experiences of those they interview.
- Ask the children to act out short plays, re-living the scenes described in the memories.

Key questions

- Whose memories are you recording?
- Did they have a happy or sad time?
- How might this affect the way they remember things?
- How can we check whether these memories are accurate?

Lines of enquiry in your locality

- Invite a visitor to the classroom to talk to the children on a topic of local history.
- Focus on a particular theme or topic. This could be as simple as an account of school days, childhood and family life or, more specifically, an historical event such as the coming of the National Health Service or a local event of significance.
- To develop an awareness of how memory can alter an interpretation of events, try playing Chinese Whispers. How did the story get changed? Make a table of your findings. The story *Wilfred Gordon McDonald Partridge* by Mem Fox (Puffin Books) tells how a boy helps an old woman to regain her memory.
- Interviewing people is an ideal method for developing questioning techniques. Pupils need to think about the range of questions they will ask. Closed questions are useful in establishing the factual background but open questions will invite the interviewee to develop a reply.

Chinese Whispers

Story 1	
Story 2	
Story 3	

Interview questions

- When did you go to this school?
- How many children were in your class?
- What were your lessons?

War memories

Heavy bombing by German aircraft was expected at the beginning of World War II in 1939. Many children were sent away from their homes to the countryside, where it was thought they would be safe. Here are some people's memories about evacuation during the war:

Your help is needed to foster these children.

'As a small child I can remember the evacuee children coming. We were horrible to them. We ganged up on them in the playground. We were all in a big circle and the poor evacuated children were herded in the middle. We shouted at them, "You made us squash up in our classrooms, you've done this. You've done that."'

Jonathan Croall

'I was separated from my close friends and was sent to live in a house with a girl I didn't get on with. The wife had been a servant and thought of us as servants. I can still remember lots of washing up and cooking. We were also very cold. The lights were very low. One night I fell down the stairs because there were no lights and had to spend a day in hospital.'

Brenda Preedy
(came from a well-off family)

'I was sent to live on a farm for over six months and enjoyed every minute of it. The first week we were collecting in the hay and there were animals everywhere. They never told you that we couldn't have anything more to eat.'

Peter Wentworth
(came from a poor family)

- Draw a blue line around those extracts in which the evacuees had an unhappy time.
- Draw a red line around extracts in which the evacuees had a good time.
- Draw a blue line under the words which tell us that evacuees had an unhappy time.
- Draw a red line under the words which tell us that evacuees had a happy time.
- What other reasons can you think of why children might have been unhappy at being evacuated?
- Why did some evacuees have a good time while others were miserable?
- These stories come from people's memories. They were grown-ups when they wrote down what had happened when they were children. What might have happened to their stories when they had to remember things that happened a long time ago?

Dear diary – Ideas page

Focus

Knowledge and understanding of historical information contained in diaries.

About the source

These diary extracts have been chosen to illustrate some of the intrinsic features of diaries.

The diaries represent different experiences of people who lived in close proximity but whose circumstances were very different. Encourage the children to consider why people's views of past events will be different from one another's.

Diaries have the value of being eye-witness accounts and often recount events whilst they are still fresh in the mind of the person. These two extracts are fascinating because they throw light on the past through the eyes of ordinary people. At the same time they represent one person's view of events and their experience may not be typical. By their very nature, diaries are not normally a readily available source. However, the local archives and local history publications may provide some examples.

Using the activity sheet

- Discuss what a diary is and who might be likely to keep one. What are the strengths and limitations of diaries as sources of the past? It should be explained that famous people will expect their diaries to be read and this may determine the content of their writing.
- Discuss how and why diaries might be kept private. Samuel Pepys, the most famous diarist, could be used as an example of how a secret code can keep the contents of a diary unknown for many years.
- Pupils could devise their own code for their personal diaries.

Key questions

- Who has written these diaries?
- What do they tell us about the sort of people who wrote them?
- Why might these diaries be useful to someone studying this period of history?
- Why must we be careful when using diaries as evidence?

Lines of enquiry in your locality

- Use the pupils' daily news books with their permission. Compare entries for differences and similarities.

- Examine collections of letters. They are particularly helpful when the replies are also available. These sources can often show us the real causes behind events rather than the public statements. The children could draw up a table comparing the two sources.

Local centenary	
Public reports	Private letters

- Look at travel journals as a useful source of information about farming, industry, towns and transport, for example the travel journals written by Daniel Defoe in 1720 and Arthur Young in the 1760s. Ask the children to tabulate their findings.

Travel journal of Defoe	
Towns	
Transport	

Dear diary

On this page are extracts from two diaries.

This is the holiday diary of a teacher from
Lancashire who went on holiday to Bournemouth.

Monday – 30.7.23	Tuesday – 31.7.23
Went to town for a film in the morning and walked to the old Saxon church in the afternoon, with baby. Rained. First time I used my umbrella since coming. Pictures should be very good. Pleasant evening.	Charabanc to Stoke beach. Beautiful ride through country lanes. Lunch on arrival. Then climbed on to rocks and waded into the sea. Photos snapped in various positions. Sheltered from short shower in canteen. Visited Revelstoke churchyard and looked at remains of church. Definitely DO NOT like the horror landlady!

- What did she do on her holiday? What subjects do you think she enjoyed teaching in school – Mathematics, Painting, History? Why?
- What subjects does she mean by 'pictures should be very good'? How did she get to Stoke beach? Do you think she enjoyed her holiday?
- What did she put in her diary which tells you no one else was allowed to read it?

Here is another diary which comes from the same town in Lancashire as the teacher.

Monday 30th	Tuesday
Joe tried every mill in town – still no work. Found a three-penny piece in the lining of his jacket. Don't know how we'll manage for rest of week.	Mill needs hands. Joe one of the lucky ones. Beef stew tonight.

- Where did Joe go looking for work on Monday?
- Where did he get work on Tuesday?
- How do you know this family is poor?
- Who do you think might have written this diary?
- What are the differences between the two diaries?
- What is the most important difference?
- At last Joe got work at the mill. 'Beef stew tonight.' If someone said to you 'Everybody in this town in 1923 was happy', what would you say to them?

Protecting the people – | Ideas page

Focus

The work of the ARP in response to World War II bombing raids.

About the source

In 1935 the government instructed local authorities to prepare plans for the protection of the civilian population. This task was not taken seriously until the Munich Crisis of 1938 when Sir John Anderson (of Anderson shelter fame) was put in charge of ARP. Local civil defence records often include accounts of bomb damage and casualties, together with the work of air raid wardens, firemen, police, rescue and demolition teams, and casualty stations. At times they can be detailed and vivid and may need to be handled sensitively. Bombing incidents may well refer to families that still live in the locality. Useful books are *Front Line 1940–41*, HMSO 1942 and *Roof over Britain*, HMSO 1943.

Using the activity sheet

- Check the children are familiar with the 24-hour clock. Use this to list the events of the school day.
- The crashing bomber in Sunderland was brought down by anti-aircraft fire. Discuss anti-aircraft defences – radar, observer posts, fighter interception, gun and searchlight teams, barrage balloons.
- How had the shelter saved the lives of the S. family? What kinds of shelter were available, for example Anderson in the garden, Morrison in the house, large public shelters in major buildings?

Key questions

- What does ARP stand for? (Air Raid Precautions.)
- The government called ARP workers 'front line soldiers' in 1940–41. Why was this?
- What dangers did the ARP staff face? Why is petrol vapour very dangerous?
- Who was in charge of the rescue? What were the main responsibilities?

Lines of enquiry in your locality

- Discuss any emergency plans for your school. What happens in case of fire or an outbreak of infectious disease? Who is in charge? What do they have to do?
- Look at a 1:2500 OS map of c.1940 for your area. (See page 13.) Are there any likely targets for enemy bombers? The Germans produced target plans based on British OS maps, with a German key. Many of these are available in local archives.
- Many ARP personnel were part-time workers or volunteers – housewives, farmers, dockers, engineers, clerks. Discuss why they might have joined (unemployed, sense of duty, protecting their home area and so on).
- Find a report of the worst raid in your area. What was damaged? How bad were the casualties? Try to compile a set of photos showing a pre-war, war damaged and rebuilt site, for example 1950s flats in the middle of a Victorian terrace. Chart your findings.

Protecting the people

In 1940, during World War II, the Germans began to bomb Britain. ARP rescue teams saved tens of thousands of lives.

● Carefully read this report:

Central Fire Station,
Sunderland.   3 October, 1940.

I beg to report that at 2319 hours, Thursday 5th September, an enemy bombing plane crashed upon 55 Suffolk Street and set fire to the nearby property. I immediately turned out with numbers 1 & 5 machines and foam apparatus.

On arrival at 2322 hours I saw that the plane had crashed into the rear of the houses. The petrol and oil from the bomber had scattered over a wide area, and being ignited, had started fires which were burning furiously. A quantity of oil and petrol was also burning under the falling debris at the back of the houses.

At about 2328 hours I was informed that 3 people were trapped in a wrecked bomb shelter, which was covered in debris. The shelter itself was on fire. I called for volunteers and we removed heavy concrete slabs and other wreckage from the shelter, thereby rescuing John George S., Rachel S. and their daughter Jean from the wreckage. When Mrs S. was rescued she was found to be dead.

During the operations a jet of water had to be played on the feet of the trapped persons which were being burned by the blazing petrol. The rescuers showed great courage in the face of flames and heat from the burning petrol, concentrations of petrol vapour and the fact that further bombs in the plane might explode.

T. Bruce, Superintendent of Fire Brigade.

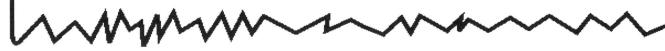

Jean and her Dad were saved just in time, but Mum had been killed. How would Jean have felt? What would she have written about this terrifying day?

● Fill in her diary:

The diary of Jean S., 4 October, 1940.

I am so shocked and upset I hardly know what to write. Yesterday,

_____

_____

_____

_____

Disasters in the newspapers – Ideas page

Focus

Using newspaper reports to learn about local events.

About the source

Newspapers are usually kept in the local public library. Most libraries have lists of the titles and dates of their collections. The growth of newspapers was restricted by government stamp duty on newsprint until 1856. In spite of this, many local papers were established in the eighteenth century and most areas of the country had their own 'local rag' by 1900. They offer teachers one of the richest sources of evidence for local people and events. For younger children, features such as adverts and letters pages may be more appealing than the news reports. Look out for and keep reprints of special editions, such as the anniversary of the D-Day Landings.

Using the activity sheet

- Explain that nitrate film used at this time was highly flammable and cinema fires all too common. The main problem, however, was that the emergency exits were locked and the children died in the crush as they tried to get out.
- Discuss why the children panicked. What would have been the safest thing to do? What would a surviving child have experienced? Write a newspaper article based on a survivor's story.

Key questions

- Why did the children panic?
- What caused the deaths?
- Was anyone to blame?
- Why did the deaths seem particularly tragic at the time of year of the newspaper article?
- How would parents feel as they heard the news?

Lines of enquiry in your locality

- What disasters/accidents have been in the local or national news recently? Make a class display or scrapbook, discussing and headlining the causes, for example human error, weather, terrorism. How could the disaster have been avoided?
- Focus on the cinema as a feature of Britain since 1930. Interview adults to find out why going to the pictures was such a treat in the days before TV. Detailed cinema features and reviews were published weekly in most local newspapers.
- Look at events in local newspapers today, fifty years ago and 100 years ago. Discuss how the designs of newspapers have changed, for example, amount of text, headlines, position of adverts.

LOCAL DISASTERS

Newspaper designs	
Today	
50 years ago	
100 years ago	

Disasters in the newspapers

In the days before television, children were thrilled by visits to the cinema. On 31st December 1929, this New Year treat went horribly wrong for the children of Paisley in Scotland.

● Read the newspaper account and fill in the report form.

69 SCHOOL CHILDREN DIE

Paisley's saddest Hogmanay

Tragedy in its most horrifying form marked the closing hours of 1929 in Scotland.

The whole country was shocked by the terrible news (contained in our later editions last night) that 69 children had perished in a stampede in the Glen Cinema, Paisley, following a wild rush which arose on the call of "Fire."

Nearly 2000 boys and girls, mostly from working-class homes, were enjoying a Hogmanay matinee performance in the cinema, when thick clouds of smoke, caused by a film which had caught alight, were swept into the theatre from the vestibule.

PANIC TO ESCAPE

Immediately the young folks fell into a panic, and there was a frantic rush to a doorway behind the stage at the opposite end of the hall.

To their horror, the children found that this doorway was closed, and many began to scream in terror.

In their frenzied efforts to escape, some jumped from the balcony, many fainted, and their bodies were trampled on.

One of the most heartrending features of the disaster is that at no time were the victims in real danger from fire. Death was mostly due to suffocation caused by crushing.

PARENTS' TRAUMA

Altogether 150 children, including the dead, were taken to the Royal Alexandra Infirmary, Paisley, where terrible scenes were witnessed.

Parents and relatives, agonised by uncertainty, crowded at the entrance in an effort to obtain news. Some women succeeded in gaining admittance and then collapsed and had to be taken out again.

Artificial respiration was applied to the victims, and several lives were saved by this means before they were hurried to the wards. Those who were not were added to the growing list of dead.

Disaster Report Form	
Place	
Date and Time	
Number of children present	
Cause of fire	
Cause of death	
Number killed	

 ● Prepare a list of safety measures to stop a cinema disaster like this happening again.

Church search – Ideas page

Focus

Churches are an invaluable resource for information about local inhabitants.

Using the activity sheet

- Discuss with the children what they already know about places of worship, for example where they are and what they look like.
- Arrange to visit a local church and divide the children into pairs of mixed ability. Observations will focus on the exterior of the building as well as the interior.
- Use the observation form on the activity page to make notes and a sketch drawing of the architecture of the building.
- Once the information is recorded, children should use the evidence to work out other information like the age of the building, interior and exterior changes and important people who lived locally.
- In groups, children should list what this tells us about changes in their local community and then they must decide which is the most important change.

About the source

Places of worship are buildings in which religious ceremonies take place. In Britain many religions exist but most of the religious buildings are for people who follow the Christian faith.

For many hundreds of years the church was the most important building in the community. They were the first places to keep records of births, deaths and marriages. Often, churches will also contain memorials to important people in the community and the graveyard can reveal names, ages and sometimes the cause of death, of the inhabitants.

Lines of enquiry in your locality

- There is an obvious connection between this activity and the study of religions. The historical emphasis ought to be on when particular faiths became established in the community and how this affected changes in other things, for example in the foods we eat, types of shops or any other discernible change.

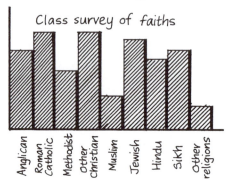
Class survey of faiths

- Make a class survey of religious buildings in the locality. The children could record the names and dates of local buildings in a table.
- Invite members of the respective faiths to talk to the children about their beliefs and the history of their faith community in the locality.
- Use a map of the local area to identify different places of worship in the community. How many Christian churches are there? Which Christian denomination has the most buildings?

Key questions

- When was the church built?
- What type of church is it? (For example, Church of England, Methodist, Roman Catholic.)
- Does it have a special connection with someone?
- Has it been altered over the years?

Church search

Outside the church

● Draw a sketch of a church you have visited.

Inside the church

● Can you find the following in your local church?

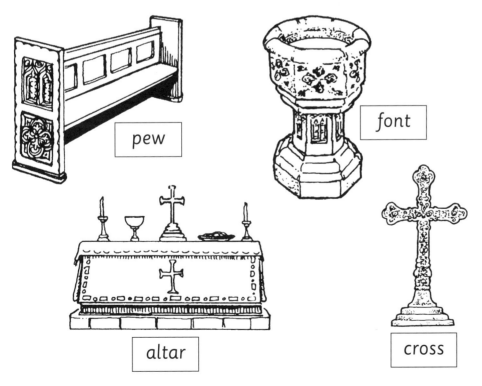

pew

font

pulpit

altar

cross

lectern

● Are there any windows with pictures in them?
Does this tell us anything more about the church?

Our streets – Ideas page

Focus

Knowledge and understanding of the development of house styles over time.

About the source

The illustrations show the range of types of housing that children are likely to encounter. Pupils should be encouraged to think about the particular features which denote the period of history to which they belong, for example a datestone, and in this way form an understanding of the age and development of their neighbourhood. Children should use symbols to describe the types of houses as well as sketching a typical house, indicating some detail. They will need to think about and discuss particular changes to the building and why such changes may have occurred.

Using the activity sheet

- Pupils need to become familiar with the various types of houses and an illustrated word wall of these names will encourage children to practise the terms.
- A survey can be conducted of the types of houses the children live in and a graph produced.

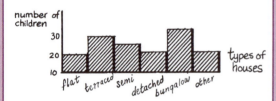

- Discuss the clues in the pictures of the houses, for example why did Victorian houses have slate roofs? Why were the Victorian houses built in terraces? Why did 1930s council houses have gardens? Why have many of the older styles of housing come back into fashion?

Key questions

- What style of house is it?
- When was it built?
- What changes have occurred since it was built?

Lines of enquiry in your locality

- Choose an interesting street which shows features of change over time or a variety of types of housing. The pupils should plot the housing using symbols and sketch one of the houses to illustrate the changes. Can they distinguish the modern from the original? What have they used as clues?
- The local council can provide maps of the area. Children can compare the street patterns which emerge in different parts of their neighbourhood and try to explain the reasons why, for example, a railway could affect street patterns.

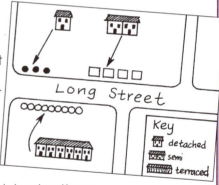

- Using maps on a larger scale, colour in the areas where particular types of housing predominate. Does this indicate how the building development has grown up for the area in which the children live?
- Where possible, use census information and trade directories to interpret the occupancy of the houses. Who lived in these houses, what did they do and where were they born?
- The local council may also have the plans of individual houses. Children should study these in detail and compare them with their own houses.
- Elevations of the plans of the houses can also be used as templates for models which the children can cut out and glue together. The street can then be reconstructed for explanation and presentation to adults and other groups of children.

Our streets

Here are some pictures of different types of houses you might see near where you live.

Suburban Victorian house for the well-off (1840–1900)

Victorian terraced houses (joined in a street)

Semi-detached houses of the 1930s

Tower block flats of the 1970s

Street survey
● Choose two or three streets and draw sketches or plans of the types of houses you can see.

Praising people – Ideas page

Focus

Knowledge and understanding of the effects of war upon a community and records of the individuals involved.

About the source

The story of public monuments in the first half of the twentieth century is dominated by the building of war memorials. The South African or Boer War was relatively small-scale and confined to that country. Nonetheless, it relied on militia and volunteers who fought alongside regular soldiers. The statue represents Victory holding the laurel crown of battle.

The huge death toll in the 'Great', or First World War produced such a profound effect throughout the country, that civic pride, coupled to the fact that nearly everyone had lost a relative, demanded a significant effort.

There are much fewer specifically built Second World War memorials. Frequently a commemoration was added to a First World War monument. In this instance, however, mention is made of women who had served their country.

Using the activity sheet

- The first question is relatively simple and requires pupils to place the three examples in sequence. The remaining questions make an attempt to tease out some of the differences between the three memorials as evidence.
- The examples also provide a stimulating starting point to find out in greater detail the differences between the three wars and therefore what impact they had on the local community.
- Explain difficult words and place on a word wall. Add the system of Roman numerals or provide the dates.

Word wall – Monuments

Decorum	–	Politeness, good manners
Desiderare	–	Regret the loss of
Pro Patria	–	For the fatherland

- Visit local war memorials to stimulate questions about each war, what information the memorial gives us, what designs are on it, why people wanted to remember the event.

Lines of enquiry in your locality

- Discuss the variety of types of monuments raised and the types of persons commemorated, for example, local worthies, disasters both industrial and natural and more recently, local personalities.
- An observation sheet can be used to record such monuments.

Who/what	
Sketch	
Writing (Inscription)	
Where situated	
Why built	
What else I found out	

Key questions

- When was this monument made?
- Why was it made?
- Who/what is it dedicated to?
- What does it tell us about how the local area was affected?
- Does it include words in Latin?
- What do they mean?

Praising people

Many British people fought and died in wars. To remember those who had died in the wars people in cities, towns and villages set up monuments. These are known as war memorials.

Here are three war memorials. Look at them carefully. The writing (inscriptions) on the monuments is large so that you can read it.

These men served faithfully in the following regiments:
Gordon Highlanders
Durham Light Infantry
Coldstream Guards

War Memorial
The Great War 1914–1918
Unveiled MDCCCCXXI

The South African War
1899–1902
Erected MDCCCCV
Dedicated to the 76
fellow townsmen
who gave their lives for
their country and empire

Pro Patria

Dedicated to the 58 men
and women of Marsons
Armaments who died
during the air raid 14
June 1941

- Number the three monuments so that the earliest war comes first and the latest war last.
- Copy and complete the table. Write down the differences between the wars in the boxes.

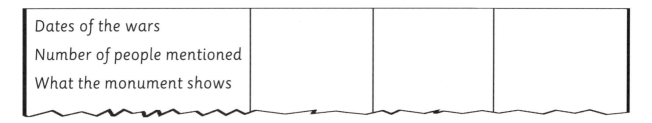

Dates of the wars			
Number of people mentioned			
What the monument shows			

- What else can you find out about these wars? How did they affect the place where you live?

IDEAS BANK – *Local History*

8 ways to help ...

There are many ideas in this book about developing and extending the photocopiable pages. Here are just eight ways to help you make the most of the **Ideas Bank** series.

1
Paste copies of the pages on to card and laminate them. The children could use water-based pens that can be wiped off, allowing the pages to be re-used.

2
Put the pages inside clear plastic wallets. They could be stored in binders for easy reference. The children's writing can again be easily wiped away.

3
If possible, save the pages for re-use. Develop a simple filing system so that the pages can be easily located for future use.

4
Use both sides of the paper. The children could write or draw on the back of the sheet, or you could photocopy another useful activity on the back.

5
Make the most of group work. Children working in small groups could use one page to discuss between them.

6
Photocopy the pages on to clear film to make overhead transparencies. The ideas can then be used time and time again.

7
Use the activity pages as ideas pages for yourself. Discuss issues and ideas with the class and ask the children to produce artwork and writing.

8
Customise the pages by adding your own activities. Supplement the ideas and apply them to your children's needs.